Hopi Candles

First published in Great Britain by
Pen Press Publishers Ltd
The Old School
39 Chesham Road
Brighton
East Sussex BN2 1NB

ISBN 1-904754-28-7

Printed and bound in the UK

Also by the author
MESSAGES FROM BEYOND THE VEIL

A catalogue record of this book is available from the
British Library

Cover design: Sheyda Navab

Hopi Candles

by

Jili Hamilton

Acknowledgments

Many people have helped me in the preparation of this little book, especially Vicky Lee, my dentist in London, whose encouragement enabled me to start writing. The support of those friends who wish to remain anonymous has been precious to me. They know who I mean. Heartfelt thanks, too, to Sheyda Navab for her help in preparing professional flyers as well as the layout and cover of this book. My deep gratitude is also due to Patrick Quanten, MD and Greg Webb, RMT who have not only given me permission to use their very interesting paper, but have also taken the trouble to read and comment on my text.

I would also like to thank Wendy Rigby for her support and professional advice at the exhibitions we attended together, Raj Vora and his team from Revital and last, but certainly not least, all my customers who have taught me so much.

For Mike

*without whose unfailing friendship and support
I would not have had the courage to go on.*

TABLE OF CONTENTS

Introduction

It was whilst living in Switzerland in the mid-1980s that I first heard the word "reflexology". A friend showed me a diagram of the reflex zones on the feet that was so fascinating I decided to study it, obtaining a diploma in 1987.

That was the start of a passion for complementary medicine; in fact it was just after obtaining this diploma that my attention was caught by an article in a magazine about Hopi ear treatment candles. The article was accompanied by a photograph of a man lying on his side with a hand holding an upright lighted taper in his ear. Very bizarre! However, on reading the article, I understood that these candles (which are hollow tubes made from linen and not exactly "candles" as we are in the habit of seeing them) could be used for a plethora of health problems. The treatment seemed to be extremely simple, consisting of lighting this tube which, when in place, functioned like a chimney, drawing and cleansing. Although it was said to work for sinusitis, otitis, impacted wax, relaxation, etc., its main aim was to improve the flow of energy to the ear by stimulating the acupressure points and the localised lymph system. Once these systems functioned properly, the production of cerumen was controlled and the energy flow normalised.

Over the years I have been using them, I can say with total conviction that they do everything they are advertised as doing and much, much more. The method has always been advertised as something anyone could perform at home, and the candles were, and are, on sale in pharmacies and health food shops. Many therapists use them and frequently combine them with other therapies, as I do myself. It is naturally worth emphasising here that all complementary therapies go hand-in-hand with a healthy lifestyle and this applies to every aspect of our lives, not only to our nutritional habits.

A couple of days after reading the initial article, I was telephoned on another matter by someone I'd met on my reflexology course. I mentioned it to her and she became very enthusiastic, recounting a few cases where she had found them hugely successful. Completely convinced, I took the name of a lady who made them and a friend, as fascinated as I was by the treatment, visited her and purchased some. I then received my first treatment, and before long was treating my work colleagues and obtaining excellent results.

On leaving Switzerland for London in 1989, I was amazed to find this therapy was not widely available there so I decided to set up a company, Hopi Products Limited, to import and promote the candles. Our first public outing in Britain was the Healing Artsm Exhibition in London in the autumn of 1991. This is the oldest and largest exhibition of complementary therapies in Britain and attracts hundreds of exhibitors and thousands of visitors from all over the world. From Day 1 we were caught up in an amazing rush of enthusiasm, with people practically standing on each other to obtain a better view! Some people attending told me that up to then they had made their own candles with more or less success, so they were delighted to find something being produced commercially that was safe and would not drip hot wax or burn a hole in their clothing.

Sales soared, and these included many repeat orders. I was frequently contacted by people who had marvellous stories to tell and, perhaps more importantly, people who couldn't find much information on them. Indeed, in the years I have been using them, I have found practically nothing published apart from a few magazine articles. That is why I have finally decided to write this little book, putting into it what I have learnt about ear treatment candles and what they can do. If it helps to introduce more people to this simple but highly effective therapy, then I shall feel it has been totally worthwhile.

CHAPTER 1

Origins

Many people who come to exhibitions express amazement at seeing a treatment that to them is something granny did when they were children. I have met people from Macedonia, Italy, in fact all round the Mediterranean basin, and Latin America, who say this was a well-known folk remedy in their home country and they are delighted to see it again.

One therapist from Cyprus told me that people in his village used paper impregnated with beeswax and honey to make candles and it was a therapy much in use even today. As I didn't at the time know why honey was used, his mother was able to tell us that it stopped the candle from burning down too fast. Rolled up newspaper or tobacco leaves have been mentioned many times and each country's traditional method grew out of its most easily-obtainable materials.

Pottery cones and even reusable glass cones have also turned up.

People from North America are very interested in the origins of ear candles (although theirs are usually conical and referred to as "cones"). Everyone seems to agree that it is a very ancient tradition stretching back for centuries when folk healers all over the world used the therapy in some form or another. The Chinese, Tibetans, Egyptians, Mayan, Aztec and American Indian cultures are always mentioned, as is the method used by the Choctaw Indians of North America, which was to blow the smoke of various herbs through a cone-shaped object into the ear canal. In China today, the ear cleaner still plies his trade in teahouses, often giving neck and shoulder massages too.

Many ancient cultures thought of coning as a spiritual practice to clear the mind and the senses. There are petroglyphs in some of the North American Hopi canyons depicting the use of ear candles, and folk art in other countries shows this too. The Hopi always use sage, which is a well-known cleansing herb, in their candles. When someone dies in Hopiland, their house is smudged with sage to purify it.

American cones use all kinds of herbs and essences, with one company using rose oil mixed with the beeswax. According to them, this particular oil has the highest vibration. They add that the human body has the potential to vibrate at 200,000 cycles per second, but as the average person vibrates at around one tenth of that, rose oil will raise the frequency.

Today's methods

By far the most widespread method of cleaning ears nowadays is syringing. This is a process whereby a high-pressure jet of water is released into the ear with the object of dislodging and extracting excessive wax, and extremely unpleasant it can be, too, depending as it does on the expertise of the practitioner. Apart from the possibility of perforating the eardrum (rare, but it does occur), people find the more they have it done the more they need it done. Perhaps the stimulus to the ear is too powerful and the cleansing too thorough, causing the body to produce more wax to compensate. This is why people frequently need more than one candle treatment—it is gentle and the amount of wax that needs to come to the surface does so only when it is ready.

A former general practitioner's nurse told me she had regularly given this treatment in the past and people could feel so light-headed after it that they were unsteady on their feet. She did add that the quality of the syringing and the degree of discomfort experienced depended totally on the person doing it.

Another form of ear cleaning is practised in India by the man on the beach with a piece of wire. In a more professional context, I have been told that German medical students learn candling as part of their training and, although it is practised by many therapists and even doctors, it is a home treatment and always has been.

The candles we use in Europe are thin, hollow linen tubes approximately 5 inches long, made from organically-grown flax. They are impregnated with beeswax, honey and herbs, notably sage. Nothing can possibly "fall down" the candle and in the base there is a small plastic ring where the debris from the ear will lodge.

People often ask if they will be burnt by hot wax, but it doesn't work like that. First, there is only a small amount of wax in the candles and second, the linen burns like any other material; it bends over on itself and has the weight of a flake of ash. Indeed, the candles are specially made so as not to drip or break. If the person being treated is apprehensive, a cardboard circle with a hole cut in the centre for the candle can be used, although most people prefer the feel of a hand placed lightly over the ear with the candle poking through the fingers.

I would add that it is important to buy properly produced candles of whatever make as one patient had received hot wax in his ear from a candle that had been made by a friend.

How the candles work

If we take the view (which physicists now seem to have proved beyond any doubt) that everything is energy, the body is no exception. When the body's energy is circulating properly all is well. However, most of us eat food that may have been treated with chemicals and is often full of sugar, fat or salt; we live in polluted environments and often have stressful lives where we rush hither and thither to get everything done. All these factors help to deplete bodily energy and then we fall ill.

One of the functions of the candles is to re-stimulate the energy around the head, ears, etc., which they do very powerfully and efficiently. This is why people who have used candles for one problem, such as migraine, have found to their delight that the sinuses may clear too. Or those who have used them for sinusitis have found their hearing improves at the same time.

Another advantage of the candles is that they stimulate the peripheral lymph system. The lymph carries the body's debris away, and when it is stimulated and flowing as it should, it enables the immune system to function better. Our lymph circulates through capillaries in the same manner as blood does in the veins, so those in the zone of the ear receive a boost from candling.

Acupressure points, which are found everywhere in the body, are also stimulated in the region of the ear by the candle treatment. If we take the shape of the ear as an inverted foetus, we can find where on the body these acupressure points are. It is said that pirates always had pierced earlobes because, representing the eye reflex, this enabled them to see ships coming over the horizon before the ships' lookouts saw them! It is also a fact that people who have piercings up the ear can suffer from liver and kidney problems, as these regions are being improperly stimulated by the hole in that part of the ear.

An extremely detailed explanation of the way candles work is given in a paper entitled *Ear Candling and Cancer Therapy* by Patrick Quanten, MD (UK) and Gregg Webb, RMT (Canada), reproduced in its entirety in Chapter 4 and I won't repeat the relevant points here.

A crystal therapist mentioned at one exhibition that, as a treatment was being given, she could see negativity being burned out of the aura (the electromagnetic field that surrounds the body) and this is one of the more subtle functions of the candle. It is why it needs to be held upright and why moving about too quickly after a treatment can cause a feeling of light-headedness. After any treatment it is important to rest for five or ten minutes to give the energy a chance to circulate properly.

Benefits of using the candles

Among the many physical conditions on which the candles have proved successful, the following are the best-known:

Age-related deafness
Candida
Excessive wax
Glue ear
Flying discomfort (when the cabin pressure drops before landing)
Hay fever and other allergies
Hearing problems
Migraines and headaches
Relaxation
Sinus problems

Stress
Swimming and diving (water lodging in the ear)
Tinnitus
Vertigo

and there are probably many more (see Chapter 2).

What constitutes a treatment

All that is needed is a pair of candles, a small bowl of water, matches, a cotton bud and some lavender cream or oil. You must ensure that you are not working in a draught, as this will cause the candle to burn down too quickly.

I start by asking the patient if he/she has an ear, or even a side of the body, that functions better. The patient then lies on the "weaker" side. The reason for starting with the "best" ear is that once the first side has been treated, the localised energy circulation is improved, making it easier to treat the other, weaker side. If the person feels there is no difference, then he or she chooses on which side to start.

One golden rule is that candling must always be carried out on both ears and the candle must be burned down to the same level each side. This is because our balance mechanism is located in the inner ear and the two sides need to receive an equal amount of burning. It is also why it is suggested, when treating small children, to mark a candle halfway down and burn half each side, turning the child without extinguishing the candle (see also Chapter 2, *Children and candles*).

Once the patient is comfortably settled (covered by a blanket and with a small pillow supporting the head), the candle is lit at the appropriate end and placed gently over the entrance to the auditory canal. When it's in place, the patient should hardly feel its presence. First time users often ask: "Is it in the ear? I can't feel it". You will know immediately if it is not in place because smoke will emanate from beneath the candle. If this happens, slightly change the angle of the candle, but if it means it is no longer upright, then gently push the patient's chin down towards the pillow and all should be well. During the treatment some people are aware of a crackling sound—it is very comforting and has been likened to lying in front of a log fire.

The candle should be allowed to burn down to a printed mark an inch or so from the end. When you reach this mark, gently remove the stub and extinguish it in the bowl of water. Then, very delicately indeed, take the cotton bud and remove any powdery substance that has come to the surface of the auditory canal. Just wipe around the periphery, as anything further in will come out of its own accord. This substance is candle residue.

Once the treatment is complete, you may massage a little lavender cream behind each ear, ensure that the patient is warm and comfortable and let him or her rest for at least ten minutes. If this is being done at home, the best time to treat is just before going to bed.

As people are normally curious to see if any wax has come out, open the unburned part of the candle by rolling it between the fingers. This serves no purpose other than satisfying natural curiosity, as it is usually the people who have very soft wax or who receive treatments on a regular basis who find the most residue. For someone who has hardened wax that has greatly impaired their hearing, several treatments are usually necessary to soften it and draw it to the surface, thus enabling the energy to circulate properly again.

Getting the best out
of the treatment

Because candling is a home therapy, it is often felt that it is not important to recreate the calm atmosphere one would expect in a professional context. However, like anything else, the circumstances in which a treatment is given and received make a great difference to its efficacy. Appropriate music can be played and the manufacturers of Biosun Hopi candles have produced a tape (or CD version) of music to play whilst candling called *Dream your Inner Healing*.

At exhibitions, there is a lot of noise and much coming and going, so it is difficult to create optimum conditions. However, I did experiment with someone who came two days running. On the first occasion he was most unimpressed with how he felt afterwards because I was alone on the stand and needed to talk to the public at the same time. The next day I ensured that my colleagues were free to answer all questions, enabling me to concentrate on him totally (which would be the setting when working in a private therapy room or candling at home). He went to sleep during this second treatment, clearly demonstrating that the conditions in which it is carried out are as important as the treatment itself.

I suggest that the person giving the treatment places his or her hand gently over the ear with the candle sticking up between the fingers; this gives a feeling of reassurance to the patient and cuts him/her off from anything that is going on around. You can lightly place the other hand on the patient's shoulder or the head—wherever it feels drawn to go.

Following the treatment, the ten-minute rest period is extremely important. This is why, when using the candles at home, bedtime is best. The energies are then free to circulate and the treatment is much more effective. Likewise, smoothing some lavender cream or oil behind the ears afterwards (and over the sinus areas in cases of sinusitis), can help greatly in this process. Some people recommend lavender oil on a tiny ball of cotton wool placed in the ear. This is such a soothing fragrance that it beautifully enhances the relaxing effect of the candle.

One morning a researcher on a well-known television programme telephoned, explaining that the production team was thinking of featuring the candles. I suggested he come to my home for a treatment to see if this was feasible. Having heard of the programme, it was evident that the idea was to hold the candles (and me) up to ridicule.

He was settled on cushions and, to his amazement, found the treatment exceedingly pleasant and relaxing, saying afterwards that his hearing felt clearer. He went on his way in a thoughtful frame of mind and no more was said about that television appearance.

Multi-treatments

A lthough the number of candles used in any one treatment seems to vary and in the US, they use several at once, I have never really recommended more than two or a maximum of four candles at one sitting, repeating this at regular intervals over a period of a couple of weeks if necessary. However, I was told about an elderly lady whose niece had used a ten-pack in one treatment. The niece had telephoned to say that her aunt was hearing so well at the end she had taken on a new, more positive lease of life (see also Chapter 2, *Age-related deafness*).

My own experience of giving two treatments together was on a therapist, who had made a specific request, as she had sinus problems. Three days later she called to say that her nose had just started streaming with a brown discharge, indicating that there was some very old stuff coming out, although it had taken several days for her body's energy to shift it.

It is as well to bear in mind that the first treatment should be given time to work, and that any aggravation of the problem afterwards is very normal in complementary therapies. This is due to the fact that healing starts from within and the source must be corrected first, running counter to the more conventional style of suppressing the symptoms as fast as possible with little emphasis on the underlying reason for them.

Also important to realise is the fact that the candle treatment and what results is often the start of a process rather than the end.

For conditions where, for example, the patient is suffering from a bad attack of sinusitis, glue ear, etc. a maximum of one treatment every day for a week is possible. However, this is rarely necessary so don't overdo it. Several years ago, I had an attack of pharyngitis, and despite sulphur inhalations, my sinuses remained totally blocked. A friend gave me a candle treatment and, as she finished the first side and I turned over, the passages popped open and stayed open.

Combined with other treatments

A homoeopathic practitioner, with several patients suffering from tinnitus, tried out the candles. She explained that homoeopathy had helped with the condition, but she had been unable to eradicate it completely. After using the candles, in conjunction with homoeopathy, the results had been much more satisfying.

An acupuncturist told of a patient who had a swollen lymph gland on her face near the ear. She had reduced it using needles, but the patient found that after a night's sleep it was often painful again. The therapist tried the candles in the hope that they would drain the lymph and this is exactly what they did, the lump completely disappearing in a very short time.

Reflexology is a treatment that goes well with the candles. Used first, it can open the body's energy channels, making the effect of the candles more powerful. Working on the meridian lines of the body, reflexology by itself is a very powerful tool in the therapist's armoury and excellent results have been obtained. For specific conditions where the candles are recommended, the combined treatment acts faster and even more thoroughly.

Massage practitioners, especially aromatherapists, frequently combine candles with their treatments and they are also used in combination with colonic irrigation.

They are sold to all kinds of practitioner and they enhance whatever therapy is being practised at the same session.

Contraindications

Perforated eardrum—this has been known to occur in rare cases after syringing. It has also been reported by people who have had their ears "cleaned"on the beach in India, which is quite common and usually done with a piece of wire. The person doing it will then show you "what came out of your ear," although I have been told there is some sleight-of-hand involved to make it appear that a large lump of wax has been removed. Apart from the risk of infection, one or two people have reported that it caused the eardrum to bleed. If the eardrum has been perforated it usually heals up quite quickly. If it doesn't, then a cranial osteopath could possibly help (see Chapter 3).

Grommets—this is the same as having a perforated eardrum, except that people don't always make the connection. Grommets are used in cases of otitis or "glue ear", when the Eustachian tubes become gummed up by a sticky liquid and the person (usually a child, but more and more an adult), develops a hearing problem. The grommet makes a tiny hole in the eardrum although, once it has fallen out, the drum should close of its own accord. I usually advise waiting 9-12 months from the time the grommets come out before using the candles; this gives the eardrum plenty of time to heal. (For more information on grommets and glue ear, see also Chapter 2, *Children and candles*).

An allergy to the contents of the candle.

CHAPTER 2

Principal uses for the candles and case histories

Age-related deafness

Elderly (or perhaps not so elderly) people may find their hearing less acute than it was. Indeed, they are often told by their families and friends that it is so. I can report good results in many of these cases which are often purely due to a build-up of wax that has hardened, although a fair number of regular treatments may be needed before an improvement is felt. Having said that, an elderly man told me on one occasion that, after just one pair of candles, his hearing had vastly improved. However, this would probably not be the norm.

To illustrate this, I would mention a therapist customer who was very keen to try the candles on her elderly father. She started by giving him a treatment once a week, later reducing it to once every two weeks, despite his protestations as he enjoyed the experience very much. After several months, he discovered that, not only was he hearing on registers his doctor had told him were lost for ever, the hearing aid he had been using was sitting at the back of a drawer (see also *Multi-treatments*).

Candida

I have never knowingly come across this condition, but I did see an article published in the United States about how candida was a major source of ear problems. As the interior of the ear is dark and slightly moist, it is not difficult to see that this could be so. The article went on to say that candling was the most effective treatment.

Children and candles

Many children and some adults suffer from otitis media, or "glue ear", as it's more commonly called, at some time in their lives. This "glue" is a sticky fluid that concentrates in the Eustachian tubes that run down the side of the jaw and can cause pain when the build up presses against the eardrum. I have been told that the Eustachian tubes in a child run more horizontally than vertically for the first six or seven years of his/her life, this being one of the reasons they are prone to blocking. Operations to drain the fluid consist of making a small hole in the eardrum and inserting a "grommet" which keeps the eardrum open and enables the fluid to drain out. Grommets are designed to fall out several months later (see also Chapter 3).

Unfortunately, this operation is not always successful and is now being practised less often. Sometimes one or both of the grommets fall out almost immediately, the hole closes up and the fluid builds up again; sometimes, even when the grommets stay in place for the required time, the problem recurs a year or so after they've dropped out. I was once consulted by a mother whose child had had five operations and was left with permanent scarring of the eardrum.

Children, before glue ear is diagnosed, often cannot hear what is said to them and tend to fall behind at school because they can't follow their lessons properly. Add to this time taken out for operations (to say nothing of the trauma), and they can be seriously disadvantaged.

Ear candles have proved to be a great success with young people; they love them, and it has been the experience of friends that their children ask for the candles when their ears start to feel uncomfortable. When mothers enquire how often they should use them, I suggest they listen to what the child wants, as he/she is the best judge. Of course, if they notice the child is suddenly hearing less well, then it's time for a treatment.

In Switzerland, where I discovered ear candles, paediatricians may recommend them in cases of glue ear. People also tend to consult their local pharmacist rather than visit a doctor and, as candles are readily available, they are often the treatment of choice.

Although a full candle each side for all ages is the norm, I find that with small children a half candle each side is often sufficient; certainly if the child is apprehensive, it is better for the first treatment. The candles need to burn down to the same level each side for the sake of balance, but if children become bored and fidgety by the end of one whole candle, they are prone to say they don't want any more.

One customer did tell me that when she needed to treat her baby (although the treatment is not really recommended for a child under the age of 12 months), she waited until he was fast asleep and then was able to use a small part of one candle in each ear.

Working with several therapies and with many child patients, a customer reported how he had heard about the candles and initially thought them rather weird and unprofessional. A friend, a homoeopath who worked at the same clinic, explained that, yes, they did look odd but they were extremely effective. He started using them on children suffering from glue ear; giving one treatment and showing the mother how it was done so that she could carry on treating at home. When he spoke to me, he was thrilled to recount that one of his child patients had just had a grommet operation cancelled as there was no longer any need for it.

The role diet plays in illness should never be underestimated, and this is particularly so in the case of children. A link between otitis media and food sensitivity was found back in the 1940s, so it's not a new problem. However, we are now seeing more and more allergies to cows' milk and cows' milk products that are all mucus-forming. Other culprits can be wheat, corn, eggs, yeast and soy. Milk from goats or sheep is often more digestible as it is said to resemble breast-milk, although an excess of any such product is not recommended. A recent study also found that over-consumption of sugar can inhibit the immune system, thus reducing resistance to bacterial infections. It is often a food the child craves or tends to eat most often that can be problematic. (See also *Allergies and the immune system*.)

Another factor was brought to my notice by a friend whose granddaughter was milk-allergic and frequently suffered from glue ear. In desperation, her parents took her to an elderly country dweller known for his healing powers. He took one look at the little girl and pronounced that she had a problem with her ears due, he insisted, to the residues of the vaccines with which she had been injected.

As an update on the vaccination of children, I recently read that allergies in later life can be traced back to the effect vaccines against childhood diseases have on the immune system.

The case of a Down's syndrome child was reported to me, as apparently these children often have very waxy ears. This little girl's mother tried the treatment on her; the child loved it and the next day wax started to seep out. Her mother was delighted to find a gentle remedy that the child liked, as her excessive ear wax was an ongoing problem.

Second-hand smoke in the home can be a major culprit in childhood ear infections. Candida may also cause a problem after antibiotic treatment. When a child is in pain, screaming and the ears are waxy, a practitioner cannot see what type of infection is involved and may tend to prescribe antibiotics to be on the safe side. This is why I recommend keeping children's ears wax-free with regular candling.

Excessive wax and poor hearing

Wax is produced as a means of trapping dust, foreign bodies etc. and preventing them from entering or damaging the ear. It usually makes its own way to the opening of the ear and comes out naturally. As wax is only formed in the outer part of the ear canal, a wax blockage usually means that the individual has been probing his or her ears with cotton buds, pencils, twisted towel corners etc. This only pushes it further in, with one of the most common causes for loss of hearing being a build-up of hardened wax.

Although most people have no problem with wax, some make excessive amounts. Indeed, it can be very embarrassing, especially for people with short hair. The candles therefore are absolutely ideal for this condition and from the feedback I have received they are an important standby for many people.

One early case of excessive wax being successfully treated was reported by an office colleague. She used candles every two weeks for two or three months and this regulated the production of wax thereafter.

As they work on the various energy points in the ear (see also Chapter 1, *How the candles work*), they slow down the production of the cerumen. People who have been operated on for a mastoid can also suffer badly with a build-up of wax. This adds to the problem of frequent headaches that occur throughout their lives.

I shall never forget one of my first customers at my first exhibition (when I knew very little about the candles), because the results were so amazing. A fellow exhibitor, she came to see if they could help with problems she had suffered since childhood when she had had a mastoid removed. Since then, she had suffered badly and received all sorts of treatment. With much trepidation on both sides we went ahead. A couple of hours later she came back to say that wax was "pouring"out of her bad ear and as she had short hair and was working with the public, it was most embarrassing. Was there something I could do to stop it? I explained that the wax needed to come out and when I saw her six months later she told me how, having used the candles again in the meantime, she had cleared up the problems that had plagued her all her life, pronouncing the treatment "heaven-sent".

Still on the subject of mastoid, another customer at a much later exhibition told me she had used the candles several times on her boyfriend and, not only had they helped clear the build-up of wax and debris that plagued him, his epilepsy was vastly improved too. This is the only time I have received any feedback on epilepsy, so I would hesitate to make any pronouncements; however it is worth a mention.

One lady reported that her hearing had been impaired for a while, which she felt was due to an excess of dairy products including one memorable summer's day when she had eaten a huge quantity of ice cream. After using the candles once, a hard plastic-like lump of wax fell out and her hearing improved dramatically.

A work colleague of mine told me that her husband had had poor hearing as long as she had known him (over 10 years), although he always denied this. When she discovered the candles, she tried them out on the family and after nine or ten treatments even he had to admit that his hearing was vastly improved.

A customer at an early exhibition informed me that, as she had had her ears syringed only a week or so before, they must be perfectly clean; however she was curious to try the candles. I removed a fairly large lump of wax from both ears and she was absolutely astonished.

Hearing aid wearers

Benefit can indeed be obtained by people using hearing aids (see also *Age-related deafness*), although it's important to leave the hearing aid out of the ear for as long as possible afterwards. This is due to the fact that the burning of the candles in itself is the start and not the end of the treatment. They encourage the energies to circulate and if the hearing aid is put straight back in, anything that wants to come out is blocked.

Flying

Something that interests many people is a treatment that can help with pain that may occur as an aircraft is de-pressurizing prior to landing. This pain can build up, especially if the 'plane is stacking, and the pressure could (although this is unlikely), cause the eardrum to perforate. I was a sufferer myself and went through agonies; nothing seemed to help, and I would stuff my fingers in my ears because the drum felt as if it would explode at any moment. Since using the candles regularly that is now only an unpleasant memory.

Frequent travellers and business people have found them to be a boon for this reason and the reaction of one of my earliest customers was: "This is one of the few things I've come across which is supposed to work and really does".

On the same subject, a customer whose husband suffered badly and dreaded flying, told me how she had bought a pair of candles to try before flying across the US with him. They worked wonders and the couple trawled Seattle, without success, to find another pair to do a further treatment before flying home. Things must have changed, because candles (or cones) are now available all along the West Coast.

Hay fever, allergic rhinitis and other allergies

We love the warm days and short nights of the summer when we can eat in the garden or picnic in the park, but for some people it is not a happy time at all; people who dread the summer and the scent of newly-cut grass. Or those who may have an allergy and can only look at a food they particularly enjoy, not daring to eat it. These are the sufferers from hay fever and all kinds of allergy which cause streaming eyes and a blocked nose; often headaches too. Pollution also seems to be one of the culprits, as many people suffering from "hay fever" live in large cities and often don't have a lawn to mow.

Nutrition is something to check out seriously here, and kinesiology (a form of diagnosis using muscle testing), can be very helpful in pinpointing allergies. Food additives are often responsible as well.

Ear candles are not going to take away the sensitivity to all these things, but they can make life much more bearable by helping to relieve some of the stuffiness. I have had many people tell me at exhibitions how they can breathe more easily when they use the candles.

When living in London several years ago, chatting to the young man helping his father in the corner shop, I discovered he was a medical student and suffered badly from hay fever. He was interested in alternative therapies; in fact he was the only student in his year taking an extra course to learn more about them. He bought a pair of candles to try and was highly impressed with the results; this after just one treatment. He assured me it was something he was going to investigate further (see also *Allergies and the immune system*).

Migraines and headaches

Migraines and headaches have to rank with toothache as the pain that is the hardest to bear. Backache sufferers would probably disagree, but there is a jangling agony, often nausea and vomiting and a whole range of horrors attached to pains in the head that make them so, well, painful.

People who experience this regularly are invariably on the lookout for something, anything, that could help them and, although a combination of treatments is probably the best option, the candles have proved to be very useful indeed.

Migraine sufferers usually have certain triggers that tell them an attack is on the way and this is the moment (if possible) to do a candle treatment and encourage the person to sleep afterwards. One customer reported that she was able to do this, so that when she woke several hours later, her migraine had passed.

Another person told me she had been in a car accident several years previously and every now and then experienced a terrible pain at the back of her head. She had tried everything, but found that only the candles could give her relief. She spoke to me in the very early days of my using the candles, but now I would check that she had tried cranial osteopathy.

Peppermint oil is very soothing, because peppermint helps the digestive system where the source of the problem may be found. I used to suffer migraines brought about by poor digestion and found that a cup of chamomile (which normally I detest), or peppermint tea could rapidly induce vomiting, thereby releasing some of the pressure.

Some migraines are brought on by stress or suppressed anger. If this is the case, it is helpful to see what sets them off and why. There are many classes in breathing and relaxation and books on the same subject that can be helpful for people who are unable to change their circumstances right away, feeling the need to stay with a situation that causes them stress or frustrates them.

Regular sleep patterns are important as is exercise and, of course, attention to diet. Although there are several classic "no-nos" such as chocolate, cheese etc., most migraine sufferers are aware of which foods cause them problems. Meals should be regular and breakfast in particular should never be skipped. Recently it has been found that dehydration plays a role in bringing on a migraine headache so, although it is important for everyone to drink no less than 2 litres of filtered water every day, it is even more necessary for migraine sufferers.

Rose-tinted spectacles are known to be helpful. These are used for children and can also be used for adults.

I have heard of a gadget called Medigen® which emits electromagnetic impulses to increase the brain's alpha waves. However, if an increase in these waves is helpful, that is easily brought about by meditation which has the effect of slowing down the beta action of the brain to an alpha state, at the same time releasing endorphins which give a sense of well-being. There are many different techniques and hundreds of books on meditation and relaxation. One very interesting book for sufferers, from a medical point-of-view, is *Headaches and Migraine* by Leon Chaitow, MD, DO.

I have also read an article mentioning research carried out on migraine sufferers, which has discovered that they often have abnormally low levels of magnesium in their system. As magnesium relaxes muscles, it may reduce spasms in the blood vessel walls, which are thought to play a part in migraine. The patient featured in the article had found that by implementing dietary changes and taking magnesium supplements, her headaches had practically disappeared.

Relaxation – stress relief

One of the most pleasant functions of the candles is that of relaxation. They are said to be used regularly in Germany by psychotherapists to calm disturbed patients before their therapy session starts.

When I first began selling the candles in Britain, people in London who had a problem were able to call me and I would go and show them how to do the treatment. On one occasion, a rather angry lady telephoned to say that the candles didn't work for her and she and her husband were now stuck with several pairs that they were unable to use. I visited them one evening and, sitting on their bed, did a candle treatment for both of them. When it was time to leave, I practically had to show myself out as they were almost asleep.

Seeking a professional design to use on my literature, I was put in touch with a graphic artist who had never seen the candles before and thought them rather a joke. I left him a pair and he promised to design me something. When I saw him a couple of weeks later, he was puzzled: "Are those things supposed to make you sleep?"he asked. I replied that they were a recommended bedtime treatment. He explained that his girlfriend had done the treatment late one evening and he slept very deeply that night. He just wondered if there was a connection…

Early on, a therapist working on a stand next to mine at an exhibition and never having seen the candles, decided to try them out. I heard from a mutual friend a while later that this girl had been going through a relationship break-up and a couple of days after the treatment, she spent a good few hours crying tears not of pain but of release, feeling very much helped in the process.

Sinus problems

Sinusitis can be such a painful and unpleasant complaint and some people find that every time they develop a cold it affects their sinuses. Dairy products are heavily implicated, as the extra mucus they create in the body is the last thing a sinus sufferer needs. Cheese and yoghurt are particularly mucus-forming and sometimes allergies to other foods such as wheat and soy are to blame, so it is very worthwhile checking for these too.

Bowel toxicity is something that has come to the fore in the last 20 years. This is really auto-intoxication by the faecal matter in the large intestine. One of its main effects is sinus congestion, so a sufferer from chronic sinus problems should look at the possibility that his bowels are causing or exacerbating the condition. This can be managed vary successfully by certain herbal mixtures, fasts, colonic irrigation or liver flushes. It goes without saying that any of these techniques need to be overseen and/or carried out by a qualified practitioner.

Personal experience of sinusitis has shown that reflexology is very effective, especially allied with the candles (see also Chapter 1, *Combined with other treatments*). The psychosomatic connection (something or someone is getting up your nose), should not be neglected either, because a friend of mine found she no longer suffered from sinusitis when she left home and the mother with whom she was always at war!

During one exhibition a lady, who was plagued with sinus problems, decided to try the treatment. She came back to the stand a couple of hours later not best pleased. "You've set off a sinus attack," she accused, adding that she had a streaming nose and a headache. I couldn't really tell her that this was an excellent result, which it was. As she had bought a packet of ten candles, I recommended that she have another treatment before going to bed and I'm very sure she felt happier after that.

As with all alternative therapies, it is possible to feel worse at first although, once that passes, the problem rarely recurs and if it does, often with much less force.

I would just mention here an operation that is sometimes performed to cut into and drain the sinuses. One or two people I have met at exhibitions have had surgery and been dissatisfied with the results. A friend in Switzerland was also operated on quite a few years back and the surgeon told her at the time that it would need to be re-done ten years or so later!

Swimming and diving

People who love swimming and especially divers, often find the balance of the inner ear is upset and they are extremely prone to ear infections and related problems. Many people have said how they have been helped by the candles, but one person I particularly remember.

Whilst I was demonstrating at the Healing Arts Exhibition in London in 1991, she stood watching in amazement saying she had never seen the candles used in public before. It transpired that she had a beauty clinic in the West Indies and various people, who had come on vacation to revel in the warm waters of the Caribbean, had consulted her about water lodged in their ears and pressure problems after a lot of swimming and diving, which was spoiling their expensive holidays. It was an elderly man, a native of the island, who showed her how to make candles, telling her that people there had always used them. She tried them, obtained excellent results and continued to use them.

Tinnitus (ringing or other noises in the ear) (see also Chapter 3)

There can be so many causes for tinnitus but, whatever is responsible, at its worst it can drive people into depression and even to suicide. Because there are so many causes, there are many things to look at. I will not pretend that the candles can cure tinnitus on their own; all I can say is that I have had good results, especially when they are combined with other treatments (see also Chapter 1, *Combined with other treatments*). However, it is perhaps helpful here to put down a number of things I have learned about this distressing complaint over the years.

Back in 1989, I met an acupuncturist in France who told me he was seeing many cases of kidney problems that resulted from loud personal stereos, as the ears and kidneys were in the same meridian line of the body according to the Chinese system of medicine. This leads us to the obvious conclusion that if the kidney energy is depleted (and excessive protein, salt or aspirin are heavy for the kidneys), this will automatically affect the ears too.

The most helpful book I have read on the subject is *Tinnitus* by Arthur White, DO. The only place where we part company is when he talks about regular syringing to keep the terrain clean. The book was written before candles were well-known in Britain and, as an osteopath, he would probably agree that keeping the terrain clean with the candles is preferable to syringing.

In *Spontaneous Healing*, Dr Andrew Weil mentions a German doctor working in a hospital devoted to psychosomatic medicine, who has had great success in treating tinnitus. In his opinion, this often comes from chronic muscle tension in the head and neck, usually associated with poor posture and stress. He has found that yoga and relaxation training, together with body work, frequently enable patients to get rid of this condition permanently.

If tinnitus sufferers report excessive catarrh, the candles will be at their most effective; again earlier comments about dietary changes also apply.

There have been several reports of how the plant *ginkgo biloba* has been helpful in treating tinnitus. It is thought that this condition is related to a reduced blood supply in the inner ear and herbalists believe that *ginkgo biloba* increases blood flow. Research into tinnitus and *ginkgo biloba* is now being carried out (see list of *Useful addresses*). It is important to bear in mind that if you are taking blood-thinning drugs, *gingko biloba* may not be suitable for you; you should consult your physician first.

Because the inner ear is made up of many small bones that can easily be displaced by a long-forgotten, even trivial, incident tinnitus sufferers would be well-advised to consult a cranial osteopath (see also Chapter 3).

Vertigo, Menières disease, Trigeminal neuralgia

Most people know what vertigo is, and Menières disease (thought to be a virus) also includes feelings of vertigo. As for trigeminal neuralgia, this is an excruciatingly painful affliction of the trigeminal nerve located in the face. I have often been asked whether the candles could work for these conditions, and apart from one customer who wrote me an early testimonial saying that she was "exceedingly delighted with the effect this (the candle treatment) is having on my vertigo/ear problems," have not yet received any feedback.

The giddiness of vertigo and the pain of neuralgia could in my opinion be greatly helped by candling and I would be interested in discovering more about this. Since writing the first edition of this book, I have seen on the websites of some of the therapists using the candles that they recommend them for these two conditions.

Psychosomatic links

The link between illness and the mind is becoming mainstream thinking and is being explored in different ways all the time. It does appear that illness frequently starts in our minds or emotions before it is evident in the body. Therefore, it follows that tracking back to what was going on when the illness first appeared can be extremely fruitful. Candace Pert, a well-known researcher on the role of the mind, in her book *Molecules of Emotion*, makes the following statement:

"The notion that others can make us feel good or bad is untrue... Why we feel the way we feel is the result of the symphony of our own molecules of emotion that affect every aspect of our physiology, producing blissful good health or miserable disease."

It is very important to remember this when hearing (or anything else) is impaired. A clear illustration was given by a lady suffering from tinnitus, who called one day to see if the candles could help her. It transpired that she lived alone with her handicapped daughter and the stress of looking after the girl without any respite wasn't helping her condition. At the end of the conversation, when I explained that the candles were unlikely to be of much use in her case, she burst out: "I can't stand it when she screams!" We talked about the idea of the distressing screams, but I don't know if she was ever really able to look at the situation from that angle.

A health-food shop owner, who is also a practitioner, called one day. A customer had complained how, on using the candles, she had felt pain in one ear. He admitted being rather abrupt with her; then he used the candles on himself and found the same thing happened. When he spoke to me he explained that it was his left side and when asked if there was any current challenge with his mother, as traditionally that side of the body is associated with the feminine, maternal aspect, he replied that he'd forgotten that and in fact had recently been dreaming of her constantly.

An excellent book on psychosomatic illness, with a section on ear problems is *The Healing Power of Illness* by Thorwald Dethlefson & Rudiger Dahlke. The questions they ask at the end of the section on ears are related to why we may not be prepared to "lend an ear" to other people, or whom or what are we refusing to hear.

Another interesting example of this was brought to my notice in a newspaper article about a Catholic priest who had always known of his homosexuality but, until he was ordained at the age of 32, had attempted to deny it. Thereafter, he had fought it and plunged into a nervous breakdown. Once again he endeavoured to hide his longings; until several months before he "came out". He described starting to experience an intense whistling in his left ear that he interpreted as his soul crying out to speak its truth. The physical suffering was intense and he decided to inform his bishop that he was leaving Holy Orders. His tinnitus immediately calmed down and at the time of the article appearing, he was practically cured.

Dr Christine Page, a doctor of medicine and a well-known writer on the connexion between mind, body and spirit, mentions in her book *The Mirror of Existence* that she relates tinnitus to people not listening to their intuition. They prefer to continue asking questions until they receive an answer that resonates with their desire for minimal disruption in their lives and little personal responsibility, thus limiting any errors they may make.

Ear infections

Although the candles seem to be widely recommended for ear infections, they would not be my treatment of choice. There is a variety of natural antibiotics on the market which clear infections rapidly, including colloidal silver,[1] kyolic garlic, and grapefruit seed oil. Although they only target the "bad" bacteria, it is always good to combine their use with a course of acidophilus or probiotics to build up the "good bacteria" in the gut. The instructions for use should always be followed closely. (see also Chapter 3).

One old-fashioned remedy I have come across is wrapping a warm clove of garlic in a small piece of cloth (preferably flannel), which has been wetted in hot water and wrung out. The heat and the active ingredients of the garlic will begin to draw out the pain and infection. Repeat as soon as the heat has gone.

Synthetic antibiotics, which are often prescribed for ear infections, should be avoided as much as possible as, not only do they work purely on the symptoms without treating the underlying cause, they also destroy the good bacteria in the gut along with the bad, and prolonged courses can adversely affect the digestive system.

---

1   This is a minuscule amount of silver floating in water and information may be found on it on various internet sites. I have also recently read *The Colloidal Silver Report* compiled by Zoe Adams which explains that colloidal silver will discriminate between the good and bad bacteria, only killing off that which is causing the infection. Having used it once for a very painful throat and once for an even more painful tooth infection, I can say that it worked very rapidly indeed for me.

Allergies and the immune system

Allergies, which offer evidence of a compromised immune system, frequently affect the nose and sinuses, and they tend to be set off by exposure to dust, pollen, mould, chemicals and food. The main culprits in the latter category are soy products, cow's milk, yeast, wheat, eggs, chocolate, citrus and beans, although when beans are eaten frequently as part of a balanced diet by vegetarians, they tend to cause fewer problems. For people who are allergic to soy products, careful inspection of labels is called for as many of them contain soy. Most commercially marketed margarines are made from soy oil.

It is also well to bear in mind that much of the food we eat is treated with all kinds of chemicals. Although in some places the choice of organic food may be restricted and is usually more expensive, I find it a good investment and it certainly leads me to eating more locally-grown fruit and vegetables when they are in season. For meat and fish too, it is important to eat organic. A colleague, whose brother farmed in Scotland, told me over 15 years ago that his family had stopped eating meat because he realised how often the vet was being called in to treat his animals.

Non-organic fish farms have a very poor reputation for heavy pollution of the surrounding seas. Salmon are fed pellets made from ground-up fish and oils, and the fish used for these usually come from the seabed where the polluted run-off from rivers accumulates, resulting in highly-toxic pellets. To this we can add the medication used in vast quantities on farmed fish to prevent them getting diseases that make them inedible. All this should cause us to wonder whether it is not better to stick to fish that has been farmed organically.

Another factor attacking the immune system came to my notice recently. Writing in a Swiss newspaper, Professor Yves Primault at the International University of Milan reminds us that the secretion of melatonin by the pineal gland is of capital importance to the immune system. His studies have proved that when this gland is subjected to a field of 100 nanoTesla it ceases to produce melatonin. This can by caused by a radio-alarm clock beside the head of the bed and, what is more alarming, he found that one minute on a mobile phone can inhibit the secretion of melatonin for a week.

CHAPTER 3

Where something else is needed

Cranial Osteopathy – Craniosacral therapy

There are certain conditions that cannot be greatly improved by using candles and this is usually where there is some kind of physical damage such as after a blow to the head, exposure to loud noise, or an eardrum perforation that never closes. This can be why many rock musicians (past and present) have constant noise in the head. Sound engineers, who spend all day with earphones clamped to their ears and people who frequent discothèques or places where very loud music is played, are invariably affected.

A lady came to consult me at a recent exhibition asking if the candles could help with her tinnitus. I asked her when it had started and if she knew what had caused it. She said that about a year before, a casserole dish had fallen on her head and, although she had asked her doctor if there was any connection, he had assured her there wasn't. It was explained that she had probably dislocated one or more of the tiny bones in the inner ear and that cranial osteopathy would be the most likely avenue to explore.

A similar experience appeared a few years ago when a young man asked the same question. We talked for a long while and during the course of the conversation he mentioned that he had injured his shoulder playing rugby at school. As his tinnitus was confined to one ear, the obvious question was whether it was on the same side of the body. When he confirmed that it was, it became evident that he had also possibly displaced a tiny bone in the ear and cranial osteopathy would probably help both his tinnitus and his old shoulder injury.

As a footnote to this section, I would mention craniosacral work. In *Spontaneous Healing*, Dr Andrew Weil writes about an osteopath in the United States who has had great success in treating children with glue ear. In only one session, where he concentrates on freeing up the sacrum, he has been able to cure the condition. His theory is that the sacral end of the craniosacral system is the one frequently "locked up" in children, probably from birth trauma. He explains this by saying that, when the sacrum is blocked, the primary respiratory mechanism is impaired. It is the force of the breath that pumps the lymphatic circulation; therefore when this circulation is restricted, the poor fluid drainage from the head and neck allows stagnant fluid to build up in the middle ear.

Clay therapy

This is a well-known treatment in continental Europe and there are many books on the subject. Clay is quite amazing—it will draw out infections and will even turn a baby improperly placed in the womb. When a poultice has been used it must be disposed of very carefully, as carelessly dumping it in the garden will kill every living thing around it,

As far as our subject is concerned, treatment invariably consists of clay poultices behind the ear and round the nape of the neck. Michel Abehsera in his book *The Healing Clay* gives in-depth information on how to do this. He includes cleansing the colon and using clay poultices on the lower abdomen as this can be highly beneficial in the case of ear infections too. He also mentions the method Raymond Dextreit uses which is a poultice that covers the ears (having first placed a small cotton wool plug in each ear to protect it). Dextreit is the author of what is considered the definitive book on clay. This has now been translated into English under the title *The Healing Power of Clay* and is a mine of useful information.

There are also books dealing with clay mixed with essential oils for an even more powerful effect. It is now much easier to obtain clay in Britain and there are different kinds for different uses. Abehsera and Dextreit also recommend taking clay internally, this being of a type different from that used externally. The best-known brand is Argiletz (check the list of *Useful addresses*) and this is now widely available.

Manual Lymph Drainage

I have recently read an article on tinnitus and the Vodder method of manual lymph drainage, where the writer affirms that it is one of the best methods of dealing with this condition. His reasoning is that MLD works on the causes of illness; improving the circulation and rebalancing the central nervous system, the latter enabling the vertebrae to realign spontaneously. Having taken an introductory course in this gentle technique, I can understand that it could be of benefit. When Dr Vodder'invented'it in the 1930s he was working in the South of France with a British patient who spent his winters there, as he suffered so badly from sinusitis in the damp English climate. Unable to relieve the patient's symptoms any other way, Dr Vodder devised a method of pushing the lymph gently along the sinuses with the tips of his fingers, draining it into the ganglions behind the ear.

It is important to find a practitioner who has learnt and understood the Vodder method, as I have come across therapists who purport to practise it, but are either not being honest or have not grasped the basic principles. It is an exceedingly gentle massage, using the tips of the fingers in a circular motion and, sometimes the palm of the hand, to push the lymph through the chain of ganglions. A heavy touch blocks the flow of the lymph so that it cannot circulate.

As mentioned above, tinnitus has multiple causes so I would not think this method on its own would work for every case on a one-size-fits-all basis. Because in complementary medicine each patient is treated as an individual, there cannot be one single remedy that works for everyone suffering from the same affliction.

I would reiterate here that one of the benefits of ear treatment candles is stimulation of the peripheral lymph system so, in effect, this is working as a localised form of lymph drainage.

CHAPTER 4

Ear candling and cancer therapy
by Patrick Quanten MD, (UK) and Greg Webb
RMT, (Canada)

Ear candling, an ancient ritual and healing art which formed an integral part of cultures such as those of the Egyptians, Aztecs and North American Indians, has found its way into our culture and into alternative medicine. Having "rediscovered" it from the Native Americans, it has captured the imagination of many through its amazing effects and its simplicity. People all over the world are astonished at how different they feel when they have been "candled". And the growing interest, together with the absolute safety of the ear candling process itself, has allowed a great variety of people to be exposed to it. This in turn delivers many personal experiences and testimonies, including those suggesting that it is of great benefit to cancer sufferers. But don't we hear that about every so-called-new treatment? Maybe so, but as regards ear candling, we can actually explain how and why it will improve your health, even when you are suffering from such a devastating disease. But first, we will have to enlighten you on the disease process which leads to cancer. And you thought that nobody knows how someone gets cancer! Think again, it has been known for a long time; and at the same time it has been vehemently denied because accepting this knowledge would turn our whole medical culture bottom up. The process which leads to disease has been known to man since the dawn of time, long before cancer was "invented". How people get ill has not and cannot change throughout the ages, the only thing that changes is the expression of the disease. So what is this disease process which has been written up in ancient texts across the globe, surviving time and cultures?

The Disease Process

In spite of common belief no disease happens quickly, no disease is acute; some expressions may be, but the process has to have been going on for quite some time before the medical profession recognises it as a "disease". Naming and labelling is extremely important to doctors, it is part of their *prevention* strategy as well as their therapeutic approach. However, diseases are caused by a persistent imbalance within the system. Rather than naming the disease, it is about recognising imbalances and correcting them before they damage the system and make us ill. Because all diseases are caused this way, it follows that essentially there are no "new" diseases, only variations of the same basic disease-causing factors.

Imbalance within the system, meaning what exactly? Well, the system (body and mind) has an unbreakable contract to keep you well, fit and healthy. It has a complete and accurate knowledge of every cellular function, every biochemical activity and every aspect of our energy system. Every second it performs billions of actions without ever making a major mistake. (Fancy our computers doing that!) If a tiny thing is not entirely right it will recognise and rectify it straight away. Trust your system to be 100% committed to your health and well-being. It will do the very best that is possible, given the material it has been handed by you. And that is where most of the time the struggle starts! For the sake of simplicity we will consider this "imbalance" as *any kind of deviation from "the norm", or from what the system considers normal*. This deviation we call **toxic**. A load of toxins puts the system out of balance; a prelude to ill-health. So, a toxin is per definition: *anything which, at that particular moment in time, the system does not need in order to maintain its health balance.* These toxins can enter the system from outside or can be entirely produced inside the system as part of the way it handles whatever life throws at it. Toxins, created internally as well as those entering the system from the outside, can be unnatural products that are alien to the system; they can be inappropriate or excessive items even though they are natural. Wrong timing, and wrong combination of actions can also result in toxins.

These toxins now accumulate in the places where they have been collected and/or produced, mostly the digestive tract. They cause very few minor disturbances such as very occasional distension, constipation, acidity, anger, indigestion, heaviness, or fatigue. As more and more toxins collect the symptom pattern will increase both in frequency and severity. However, all the symptoms are vague and are quickly dismissed because *everybody complains of those things and you just have to live with it.*

As the collection site is getting fuller an overflow will occur into other parts of the body causing a different set of symptoms. Depending on the organs and tissues that are affected one can suffer from complaints such as dry skin, stiff joints, headaches, cough, constipation, lack of energy, swollen glands, fever, vomiting, dizzy spells, diarrhoea, tummy pains, etc. These symptoms occur more persistently and doctors will now start to take notice. However, *all the medical tests will come back as normal.*

Those sites that are the weakest and most vulnerable will suffer the most. These particular locations will start to show signs of being unable to cope with the increasing amount of toxins coming their way. Symptoms will now be fixed in certain positions, corresponding with the troubled organ or tissues and it is at this stage that *the doctor declares you have a particular disease* such as asthma, diabetes, arthritis, cancer or whatever it may happen to be. Finally we can all be happy because they have found out what the matter is with you. Congratulations, you have just graduated from hypochondriac to patient!

Further accumulation of toxins will induce a more widespread breakdown of tissues which is generally known as the disease complications.

Cancer

Cancer has many causes, as we all know, including our toxic environment, devitalised foods (produced and sold by the food industry), sedentary lifestyle (lack of appropriate exercise), and lack of spiritual purpose or effort in life. Its basis is often suppressed emotion or emotional stagnation, which causes accumulation of toxic material, the manifestation in physical (chemical) form of feelings. This was well known in the early days of western medicine when cancer was described as a disease of melancholy or black bile, which also translates as suppressed emotions. Hence, physical remedial measures are usually not enough to restore health, as our current track record in cancer treatment confirms.

The build up of toxins happens because the digestive fire and other energy sources are low. When there is little energy available to digest and absorb food, a rotting process starts from within the food in much the same way as it would when you leave food items for any length of time. The fermentation is responsible for the bloating, the distension of the abdomen, for constipation and/or diarrhoea. These rotten products—toxins—have to be dealt with by the system which quickly makes them safe and "stores" them. As there is an almost constant influx of toxins because of the continuing low inner energy, the accumulation grows larger almost by the day resulting in major stress on the system, which eventually will lead to a collapse when it is no longer able to cope with the workload.

Effective treatment as well as prevention has to concentrate on the increase of inner energy and digestive fire. No treatment can be effective without it. Ear candling as a treatment has proven itself time and again as a very efficient method of increasing the quantity and quality of "inner energy".

Ear Candling

How can sticking a hollow candle in your ear and burning it do you any good at all?

The crucial factor is the heat that is generated by the flame. There is no direct heat exchange between the candle and the body (the ear) of the person as the bottom of the candle never even gets warm. Yet the heat on the top of the candle is just as important as the heat in the open fire burning in the winter. You do not need to sit in the flames in order to absorb and benefit from the heat produced by the flames. The reason for this is radiation; the air around the fire warms up and transports that heat to the air which is in contact with your body. As the air immediately surrounding you warms up you become warm and feel cosy.

In a similar way, the fire on top of the candle heats the air *inside* the hollow candle. This creates a movement of air as the top part of the air column is much warmer than the lower regions. The warmer air starts to spiral downwards towards the bottom of the candle (observed by anybody who has ever done ear candling), taking with it the energy from the fire rather than just the warmth from the air. In the example of the open winter fire the air moves linear from the fire to your body and creates a direct heat transfer. In ear candling the air moves spirally whereby the air molecules in that particular motion transfer the heat (temperature, kinetic energy) from the top into an ever increasing vortical movement, which cools the air but highly charges it. So, the temperature of the air moving quickly down inside the candle is cool but the energy is high. When this air now comes close to the layer of air-body contact it releases that energy into the body. It is this energy input which will make all the difference to the state of health of the body.

Yet another view of how ear candling transfers healing energy to the human body is to draw a parallel with the ancient Chinese practice of moxabustion, which is a type of treatment performed by acupuncturists to stimulate energy into systems of deficiency, creating an improved level of health function in the corresponding area. The herb mugwort is compressed into a finger thick cylinder shape, of which one end is set on fire. This end is held either proximal to the area requiring stimulation or over an acupuncture point relating to the area. Ear candling is equally about having a flame, which creates and transfers energy, close to an area and acupuncture points relating to areas in need of healing. The region in which the ear candle is burning (the ear) is a complete acupuncture point diagram of the entire body in the shape of an upside down foetus. One could easily conclude that there would be a marvellous influx of energy into the whole of the acupuncture meridian system.

Methods of studying the effects of ear candling

The authors have used various methods of research to obtain a clearer understanding of which systems are affected by ear candling and to what extent. The primary methods are active observation of clinic results and improvements in a variety of health conditions: kinesiology muscle testing (Touch for Health) and live blood cell analysis.

Live blood cell analysis is a marvellous tool to use in regard to treatment studies. It clearly shows in an almost snapshot manner the state of health of our being as well as revealing health tendencies a person has experienced through various periods of life. One observes under very high magnification the blood and its constituents on a live one blood cell-thick layer preparation. The health of our blood cells, the presence of foreign pathogens and the activity level of the cells, in particular the immune cells, can be directly evaluated. The cells of the immune system become much more active following ear candling treatment. They seem more able to sense the presence of foreign toxic material, move towards it with much greater speed and accuracy, and engulf the material with much greater ease. This fascinating direct observation helps to confirm why so many people note a rapid improvement after ear candling.

These visual findings have been confirmed in more detail through muscle testing. Kinesiology muscle testing (Touch for Health) is utilised by health professionals all over the world. The application of muscle testing is done by the practitioner pressing on the clients limb to ascertain if that particular muscle holds steady (locked) or lets go (unlocked). As every cell and every part of the body holds all information about everything that the system has ever experienced, the muscle will also have this"data base"at its disposal. The scope of information gained through muscle testing is only limited by the knowledge and skills of the practitioner and the desire to unearth true answers. It is thus that kinesiology confirms that not only the function of the white blood cells has become more precise and effective, but also that other aspects of the immune system have improved tremendously. All lymphocytes', phagocytes', T-cell and B-cell activity is more targeted and direct, as well as improvements in the function of the spleen and thymus glands. The whole of the immune system is more alert, more mobile and more assertive after each ear candling session.

Effect on Body Systems

We all know that it is crucial in cancer treatment to maximise the immune system's potential. By destroying or inhibiting the function of the body's natural fighting mechanism we will leave the body weak and vulnerable, unable to defend itself. If ear candling is going to be of any use at all in cancer treatment it will at least have to provide support for the immune system, as indeed all cancer treatments should—unless you are not particularly bothered about the effect of the treatment on the whole patient.

Visual findings of improvement in immune function have been confirmed in more detail through muscle testing (kinesiology). Not only has the activity of the white blood cells become more precise and effective, other aspects of the immune system have also improved tremendously. The overall effect is that the whole of the immune system is more alert, more mobile and more assertive after each ear candling session.

Lymphatic drainage, which apart from being an

essential tool in the clearing out of toxic material also houses a vast array of immune cells, improves significantly with ear candling. Dramatic visual descriptions of swollen lymph glands disappearing under ear candling treatment as snowballs in the sun have been reported. More commonly diffuse lymphatic swelling in the neck and throat area has been seen to disappear after treatment. Even finger swelling has diminished as reported by individuals because of loosening of rings they wore. The initial drainage is most notably seen in the area from the ears upwards, including the cranial cavity, the sinuses, the area around the eyes, the middle and inner ear areas. This also establishes an unblocking of the cranial sutures (blockage of these causes a lot of problems as demonstrated in cranial osteopathy), a re-establishment of the articulation of the cranial sutures and of the smoothness in rhythm of the cerebral spinal fluid pumping mechanism as well as the cranio-sacral articulation pump (again, such problems highlighted in osteopathy). Further sessions drain the lymphatic system from the collarbone up; from the mid-chest up; from mid-abdomen up; down to the thighs and working its way towards the toes until the entire body's lymphatic system becomes really clear and functioning. Not only does this indicate the role ear candling plays in the cleansing of the body but it also shows the accumulative effect of regular ear candling sessions whereby the cleansing of tissues continues down the body structure, rather than having to start from scratch each time when we allow too much time to lapse between sessions.

A commonly recommended treatment schedule is 3 treatments of 2-4 candles per ear within 10 days. Three additional treatments of 2-4 ear candles per ear over the next 3-4 weeks. The number of candles per ear depends upon body size and level of congestion/illness. The bigger and sicker a person is the more they will benefit from additional candles in each treatment. After this 6 treatment protocol re-evaluate and proceed as required aiming for 3-4 bursts of 2 sessions back to back per year. This will build a very strong level of health within the person on many levels.

With almost absolute predictability the healing energy delivered to the body by the ear candling process will be delivered to the systems most in need. The body is a completely conscious being, knowing precisely what is happening with every cellular structure at all times. It will therefore provide the largest amount of corrective power to the systems in greatest need, a balancing effect to the areas less in need, bringing virtually all systems to an even platform of function, then raising the capacity of function across the board up to an optimal health level. In other words, what is most urgent will get the extra energy input first, and sometimes it isn't at all where we would have expected it.

Emotional Effect

Research in the last two decades has been able to demonstrate not only the fact that emotions influence our state of health but also that all feelings and emotions are translated into chemicals in all systems within the body. When people are in a stressful state their bodies biochemically produce stress-related chemicals. These chemicals have health reducing effects such as: the stomach produces more acid and the duodenum more digestive juices in an erratic way, the mobility of the stomach and gut increases dramatically, the circulation is constantly kept high, the breathing becomes much more rapid and shallow. This serves to reduce the digestive fire for the burning of the food we consume, leading to a toxic build-up. The senses are heightened, the adrenals show a massive increase in activity, muscles are in a state of permanent tension, and so on. Stress also changes the blood flow patterns in the brain, in the limbic and endocrine systems draining blood away from those centres most responsible for clear cognitive emotionally balanced states of living. On the other hand, when a person is calm, peaceful, in a loving-centred state, that state of mind produces positive healing chemicals.

Parts of the endocrine system which are more active in a relaxed calm state will be primarily, the pineal gland, the pituitary gland, the thalamus and the hypothalamus. Both states, stressed and relaxed, result in neuro-chemical activity: one producing highly toxic substances, the other very powerful healing chemicals. We have the ability to choose through our thoughts and actions the state we live in, stressed or relaxed. **We do have the choice!**

When a person is joyful, calm, peaceful, in a loving-centred state, that state of mind produces positive healing chemicals. Parts of the endocrine system, which are more active in a relaxed calm state, will be primarily: the pineal gland, the pituitary gland, the thalamus and the hypothalamus. The amygdala and hippocampus (two parts of our limbic system controlling primal behaviours which monitor the presence of danger and sensory information, as well as mood control) will command less control in a relaxed, calm state. Chemicals, produced as a direct result of our emotions, are responsible for how we physically feel. It is the long-term direction which these chemicals give to the tissues they govern that will produce either a long, well-balanced, non-stressful cell life or a disrupted, unbalanced, damage-inducing life. Cancer is certainly one of many eventual outcomes of a long-standing stressful and unbalanced cell stimulation or suppression.

A well-documented and universally agreed effect of ear candling is a feeling of complete relaxation. People always comment on how they could "go to sleep" even during the treatment. This state produces the appropriate chemicals to reverse any negative and stress-induced effects which the body may have been living under for a considerable time; in other words, a *healing state*. The overall benefit on the health of the person in view of the above is now obvious.

W.A Chapman's book *Your Cosmic Destiny* in which he describes experiments in the psychology laboratory that found hatred, anger and jealousy caused different coloured condensates from calmness and contentment, which upon analysis contained deadly poisons. The poison of a few minutes jealousy is enough to kill a guinea pig. An hour of hatred produces enough poison to kill 80 guinea pigs; on the other hand, happy, loving peaceful emotions produce some of the most powerful healing chemicals known to mankind. If you have somebody who is in the cancer therapy treatment protocol, the thing which causes cancer to grow faster than anything else, is fear. If a person is fearful, there is an automatic fight/flight state which is prolonged for the whole time the fear resides within. The adrenals as well as the amygdala and hippocampus will be kicked into a very high functional level and the chemicals produced in the body as a consequence will be of a very toxic nature. Ear candling will instantaneously normalise the level of over-excitement in the function of these glands while dramatically boosting the systems that are in a low energy state—the pineal, the pituitary, the thalamus, the hypothalamus—systems responsible for producing very powerful healing neuro-chemicals. Ear candling instantly affects the entire glandular system and brain region energy distribution in a very positive manner. Within the space of a few treatments ear candling works to bring the entire glandular and limbic system to a very harmonious, ideal state of function. This is commonly achieved by the sixth session. As a result people are more emotionally balanced; they are more enabled, feel more capable, relaxed, less threatened, and have more hope. Hope is a powerful "molecule".

The Life Force and Healing

The energy systems of our being; aura, chakras and meridians interface with our body's electrical system, the nervous system. The intertwined function of this group provides the electrical grid that delivers life force energy to *all parts* of our being, to each cell of our body. If the energy grid experiences disrupted flow, then a direct result will be a reduction or a disturbance to the function of the particular physical part supplied with this "less than optimal energy". This will directly reduce the health capacity of that part of the body. On the other hand, strengthening the energy systems provides us with excellent resistance to ill health.

In Chinese medicine the key factor to health is a strong balanced acupuncture meridian flow carrying *chi* "life force" to all body parts. In particular the kidney organ/meridian *yin* energy is seen as a vital store-house of life's energy. Strengthening the state of kidney energy and its distribution is essential to any form of healing process. Clinical research has shown that, of the systems receiving healing energy from ear candling, the *yin* aspect of the kidney meridian is very often in the top three. This whole concept is of extreme importance to our health and it is no surprise that in Chinese medicine the ears relate directly to the kidneys. Cold is damaging to the kidneys. With ear candling the heat of the flame creates a reverse flush of energy back down to the kidneys filling them with warmth and vitality, providing a storehouse of "life energy".

In Indian medicine it is the flow of *prana* "life force" which determines the capacity for vitality in all body parts and aspects of our lives. The central part of the Prana movement, the "spine" as it were, is from the base of the physical spine upwards in a kind of double helix fashion around a central straight channel. The chakra at the base of the spine, called the root chakra, houses the "life energy" and therefore has a very close connection with the physical body. It provides it with vitality and strength, and relates to our survival instinct and procreation. The root chakra has been shown to react very quickly and positively to ear candling, gaining power and strength. From here, more energy will be distributed all the way up the spine fanning out into all body tissues. The upward movement of this energy, our life force, travels into the brain region, stimulates key areas, and then opens and strengthens the crown chakra. This chakra—the place of the fontanel (soft spot on a baby's head)—provides us with access to the universal healing energy (*yang* energy).

We find evidence of this in clinical research showing the posterior aspect of the pituitary gland (a *yin* consciousness building centre) to be the most common priority system to receive healing energy from ear candling. Clients often develop a greater inward strength and self-knowledge from continued applications of ear candling (*yin* consciousness), often translated into less fear and greater personal assurance.

The free flow of "life energy" is enhanced as a result of ear candling, clearing and strengthening all aspects of the chakras, meridians and aura. Hence the entire energy grid is much improved in its ability to deliver life force energy to every cell in our body. Cells in a state of ill health will rely on the powerful input of this life force energy to be able to regain health.

Conclusion

As shown, illness is created by long-standing stress on the natural processes. The cumulative effect of this situation leads to physical malfunctioning, such as cancer. As the only thing that caused the disease is the body and mind itself, so it is the only thing that can ever heal it. The healing will have to come from within, and can only be achieved by supporting and sustaining a natural balance within the functions of the whole body-mind person.

In order to relieve the stress caused by progressive malfunctioning one has to clean up the system as best one can. This can be achieved through stimulation and support of the elimination systems. To this effect it is essential to reduce the negative influences and build-up of toxins, to strengthen the immune system, and to increase elimination. All of these processes require extra energy input. Ear candling not only delivers that extra energy, it also mobilises the immune system throughout; it increases lymphatic drainage allowing areas to be cleaned up; and it delivers through positive mood changes a series of balancing chemicals which bring the whole systemic function back into a smooth operation, creating an environment conducive to healing and the building of health.

Patrick Quanten, MD works as a teacher and therapist all over the world, having developed his own techniques of bodywork, using only natural healing methods and traditional skills which consist of stimulating the body's healing system. He is at present setting up a project in Thailand and you can find out more information about his work on his website: http://freespace.virgin.net/ahcare.qua/index.html.

Greg Webb, RMT lives and works in Calgary, Canada, teaching Touch for Health and Ear Candling. He has a very deep understanding of kinesiology and the application of this skill to enhance the communication system with the body.

CHAPTER 5

Channelling
on ear candling/coning

This section has been added to provide information for people who are interested in the more esoteric origins of candling.

Channelled *by Eleanor Bucci, Spiritual Consultant in 1991 for the Jane Joy Foundation, Sedona, Arizona*

"Ear candling/coning can be understood as an ancient healing modality—Atlantean, Mayan, Egyptian, Tibetan—which has many other healing practices, (including time) periodically spent in "hiding". It was originally used in conjunction with initiation practices for spiritual leaders in order to strengthen their positions as bearers of great truths and as beacons of light in the darkness. Ear coning was used to open the spiritual centres and to clear and cleanse the physical as well as emotional and other auric bodies. It was used in conjunction with other healing practices and assumed a co-creative position with these practices. Traditionally, conings were performed by master energetic healers who worked on the physical as well as intermediate planes.

"Conings were performed in the temples and usually occurred in a series of three, spaced strategically apart. The number of conings performed was individualised and depended upon either the amount of clearing which was necessary and/or the spiritual appetite of each person. Although seven conings were average, at times as many as eleven conings were performed. Nine and eleven conings were considered to be aligned with the master numbers in numerology. Receiving nine or eleven conings symbolized achieving human perfection toward universal service.

"Ear conings worked upon the physical body by detoxifying the sinus, lymphatic and other systems. Among other things, they provided clarity of hearing and vision, improvement in the sense of smell, taste and color perception as well as emotional stability and mental functioning. In addition to working upon the physical body, coning worked directly with the chakra system to clear and strengthen the auric bodies as well. Traditionally, the first seven conings worked to clear and strengthen the physical body and the first seven layers of the auric field. Each coning would always affect the physical body and then affect whichever auric layer most needed to be cleared at that moment. For example, the first coning affected the physical body and either the first auric layer (etheric body) or the second auric layer (the emotional body) or the third auric layer (the mental body-thought forms) or the fourth auric layer (the astral body) or the fifth auric layer (the etheric template-associated with sound healing) or the sixth auric layer (the emotional level of the spiritual plane) or the seventh auric layer (the mental level of the spiritual plane-past life band and present life plan).

"In Egypt, however, at various times auric bodies were intercepted and provoked to release blocked energy in a sequence. For example, the first coning affected the physical body and the first auric layer, the second coning affected the physical body and the second auric layer and so on through the first seven conings. The eighth, ninth, tenth and eleventh conings were performed in order to clear and strengthen the physical body and those bodies in the cosmic plane of existence—those crystalline bodies composed of extremely fine, high vibrations. These conings were thought to totally purify the physical body and to fine-tune the auric field in order to allow one to resonate in the purist form in preparation for supreme service.

"It must be realized that coning was done simultaneously and coordinated with advanced healing practices using color, crystal, sound, and other soon-to-be-revealed methods, to correct the obstructed natural flow of energy, balance the system, realign the spinal structure and cleanse the body. These healing processes ritualistically purified individuals, allowing them to resonate to the highest vibrational frequencies. Realize also that upon your earth plane at this time, the number of conings required by individuals will be directly related to any other healing processes to which they are simultaneously exposed.

"We thank you for requesting our explanation of ear coning. We are most pleased to assist in bringing this to an understanding as now truly is the time for this, as well as other healing practices, to be more fully understood. Blessings to you."

Channelled *by Ishta Whitecloud in 1992 in Sedona, Arizona*

"Spiral leading into the etheric realm.... there are apparently etheric beings whose specific job is to oversee coning work (word "ear" is not appropriate)... oversee the turning of direction. They're like devas of that realm. So it is when someone has earache or ear trouble that we come across, we need to call on these devas and let them assist in giving us information about the best thing to do. To see what is appropriate. Because it is not always just a coning that may be appropriate. There may be hand movements (some words are inappropriate to their thought patterns), or maybe massage or holding the hand over the ear. They don't call it "ear". A person who has this problem has a loss of his sense of direction and it is some place in the turning of direction that they lose perspective of their direction.

"These etheric beings are in charge of keeping that turning on track. However, if they're having trouble with their density of vibration, that turning can be off centre. They have a sense of feeling sick or nauseous, earache or sinus problems. So to assist people on a whole level it isn't just about coning the ears. It's about assisting them in the turning of direction, about aligning that person and assisting them in making that shift.

"Remember the whole person and so, when coning, ask for their assistance because they can help. This is their job. Move your hands over the whole body. Ask for their assistance in creating a direction for this person, balance the direction, smoothing out the direction in their change. Change, change is the magic word. Assisting them in their change.

"The word coning is inappropriate for us to use. Let's see what they suggest. There really is no word in our language that is appropriate because it is a matter of tone that they work with. So to call it even a name in a sense to try to describe it, suggests a certain procedure that is only related to the ears. We could use a phrase like... 'assisting in change of direction, assisting in movement, assisting in hearing sound, assisting in opening the crown chakra'. The tone of our language is so difficult on hearing. Sometimes we use words and phrases over and over again and the tone is inappropriate to the thing that we are trying to do. When you hear a sound the spiral of the ear carries that sound spiraling through the whole body. So when we're doing this work on someone, we need to visualize that spiral of smoke or just an etheric spiral going through the whole body and lifting the direction of that person, balancing the direction, shaping the direction. So that when a person leaves us, they have a sense of balance and direction.

"I'm going back now through the files of different cultures to see what was going on in the past...... The Egyptians used the procedure inappropriately. It was used more as an elite object of power. To assist in raising power more than for any other purpose. The Tibetans used a cone but they didn't burn it. It was a small metallic cone that was placed near the ear but not in the ear, to a certain alignment with a line that corresponded to the body but also corresponded to something cosmic. They used sound near the cone to penetrate the metal that also went out and in at the same time. For them it was a connection to the cosmos bringing a balance of both coming into the body and reaching out at the same time. Only certain people had the strength to be able to have this done. Because of the sound that was carried through the whole body and the connection with the cosmos at the same time, the vibrational hit was very intense and would bring them into the next level of their being... like that (snaps fingers)!

"There's a tribe of Indians in Florida that used something similar. A stick that they'd light on the fire and place within the ear and then chanting would be done... accompanied with sound, intense sound, at the same time. Its purpose was shamanic. This person was going through an initiation for doing shamanic work. This was a very intense experience for that person and could kill them if they were not ready for it. The same with the Tibetans. Because the sound shifted the vibration of the person so dramatically and the sound going into the ears at the same time was penetrating the brain and opening the crown chakra, it could drive them crazy if they weren't ready for it.

"There's an African tribe half way down the West coast. They would pack the ears with mud to block out sound so that the person heard no sound for long periods of time and could go inward. Again, a turning in direction, an initiation of some kind into the healing arts, the shamanic. So the message is that the whole purpose is a change of direction for each person who comes. They're being initiated into the next spiral. That's why it's important that they be ready for that change."

NB I have tried to trace the two people who channelled these messages to ask their permission to use the material, but without success. I have therefore gone ahead as the messages are of such interest and, I feel, pertinent to the contents of this book. I hope that Eleanor Bucci and Ishta Whitecloud will accept this message as my heartfelt thanks for their work.

USEFUL ADDRESSES

All postal enquiries to the following addresses must be accompanied by an SAE. (NB: When telephoning from outside the UK, please use your country's dialling code for the UK and remove the first zero in each telephone number given below.)

Acupuncture

This is a treatment that restores the flow of energy and very fine sterile needles are used at precise points in the body.

British Acupuncture Council
63 Jeddo Road, London W12 9HQ
Tel: 020 8735 0400 / Fax: 020 8735 0404
E-mail: *info@acupuncture.org.uk*

Aromatherapy

Essential oils, blended just for you, are used in various ways such as inhalation and baths, but more frequently in massage. The blend of oils works on the difficulties you are experiencing at the time and the treatment is wonderfully effective for stress.

The International Federation of Aromatherapists
61-63 Churchfield Road, London W3 6AY
Tel: 020 8992 9605 / Fax: 020 8992 7983
E-mail: *office@ifaroma.org*

Bio-Cranial Osteopathy
Very gentle osteopathy which concentrates on the head, neck and shoulders.
The International Bio-Cranial Academy
PO Box 44
Bangor
County Down BT20 3SY
Tel: 01247 270626

Colonic Irrigation or Hydrotherapy
This is a gentle way of cleansing the large colon by removing the toxins and accumulated matter stuck to the sides.
The Association and Register
of Colon Hydrotherapists
www.colonic-association.org

Cranial Osteopathy
So gentle as to be almost imperceptible, this is a method of releasing resistance of bones, tissues and fluids, enabling the flow of energy to be re-established.
International Cranial Association
478 Baker Street, Enfield, Middx EN1 3QS
Tel: 020 8367 5561 / Fax: 020 8202 6686
E-mail: *kbs07@dial.pipex.com*

Kinesiology

One of the few diagnostic tools in alternative medicine; a system of muscle-testing to discover imbalances of energy in the body. Very effective for diagnosing food and other allergies.

The Association for Systematic Kinesiology (ASK)
47 Sedlescombe Road South,
East Sussex TN38 0TB
Tel: 0845 020 0383
E-mail: *admin@systematic-kinesiology.co.uk*

Manual Lymph Drainage

A gentle massage of the lymph along the capilliaries to be drained through the ganglions. This has a very positive effect on the lymphatic system.

MLD UK
PO Box 14491
Glenrothes
Fife, KY6 3YE
Tel/Fax: 01592 748008
E-mail: *admin@mlduk.org.uk*

Reflexology

A manual treatment which is used mostly on the feet but can also be used on the hands, where reflex points correspond to every area in the body. If an organ is working sluggishly, this will be reflected in the foot or the hand and the therapist will massage to clear the blockage.

Association of Reflexologists,
27 Old Gloucester Street, London WC1N 3XX
Tel: 0870 5673320 (Overseas: 01823 351010)
Fax: 01823 336646
E-mail: *info@aor.org.uk*

Tinnitus

For more information on the trials carried out on the role of ginkgo biloba in the treatment of tinnitus, contact:

The Ginkgo Information Centre
PO Box 29
Battle TN33 9ZY

Umbrella Organisations

The British Complementary Medicine Association (BCMA)

PO Box 5122,
Bournemouth,
East Sussex BH8 0WG
Tel: 0845 345 5977

The Institute for Complementary Medicine (ICM)
PO Box 194, London SE16 7QZ
Tel: 020 7237 5165 / Fax: 020 7237 5175
E-mail: *info@i-c-m.org.uk*

UK distributors of Biosun Hopi ear treatment candles
and of the tape / CD entitled *Dream your Inner Healing*:

Revital
Mail order hotline 0800 252 875
E-mail: *enquire@revital.com*
http://www.revital.co.uk

Retail shops at:

Revital Health Centre
78 High Street, Ruislip, London HA4 7AA
Tel: 01895 629 950 / Fax: 01895 630 869

Revital Health Shop
35 High Road, Willesden, London NW10 2TE
Tel: 0208 459 3382 / Fax: 0208 459 3722

Revital Health Place
3a The Colonnades, 123 Buckingham Palace Road,
London SW1 9RZ
Tel: 0207 976 6615 / Fax: 0207 975 5529

Revital Health & Beauty
12 The Highway, Station Road, Beaconsfield,
Bucks HP9 1QQ
Tel: 01494 678787 / Fax: 01494 671178

They are able to supply all the products mentioned and may also be able to give you details of a practitioner using ear candles near you as well as information on therapists who organise professionally-recognised courses in candle therapy.

Reading List

Headaches and Migraines by Leon Chaitow, MD, DO., Thorsons (The new Self-Help series) (1986).

Tinnitus by Arthur White, DO., Thorsons (The new Self-Help series) (1986).

Spontaneous Healing by Andrew Weil M.D., The Ballantyne Publishing Group.

The Healing Power of Illness by Thorwald Dethlefson & Rudiger Dahlke, Element Books Ltd (1990).

The Mirror of Existence by Dr Christine R. Page, The C.W. Daniel Company Limited.

The Colloidal Silver Report compiled by Zoe Adams, Another Country Verlag, Riemannstr. 7, D-10961 Berlin.

The Healing Clay by Michel Abehsera, Swan House, Brooklyn N.Y.

L'argile qui nous guérit by Raymond Dextreit, Vivre en harmonie, Avenue Fief, 953210 Saint-Ouen-l'Aumône, France.
(NB: This book (the English title of which is The Healing Power of Clay), can be found in any good bookshop).

*Quotation from **Molecules of Emotion** by Candace B. Pert Ph.D (with an Introduction by Deepak Chopra) by kind permission of Simon & Schuster UK Limited, London.*

About the author

Jili Hamilton was born in England and has done a variety of jobs, including secretarial work, office administration, translating, bookselling, waitressing and chamber-maiding. In 1987 she studied for a diploma in Reflexology with the Bayley School in Switzerland and this opened her eyes to the world of complementary medicine, leading her to study many different therapies including reiki, Indian head massage, metamorphic massage, lymphatic drainage, etc. In 1991 she set up Hopi Products Limited, launching ear treatment candles on the British market at the Healing Arts Exhibition in London the same year. She subsequently demonstrated and gave talks on Hopi candles at all the major health exhibitions in England and Scotland. The French translation of this present book, *Les bougies Hopi*, was published in France and Switzerland in 2003 by Editions Vivez Soleil and is available on *http://www.amazon.fr*.

Jili, who works as a teacher, spiritual healer and translator, now lives in Switzerland. She has also edited a book entitled *Messages from Beyond the Veil*, containing spirit writings by her grandmother, available from *http://www.amazon.co.uk*.

Disclaimer

Ear candling is not considered to be a medical treatment, and no claim of this nature is made. Always read and follow the directions provided with ear candles or seek guidance from an experienced ear candle practitioner. All information contained in this book is intended to increase knowledge of candling, its origins and uses, but is not a substitute for medical advice or treatment for specific medical conditions.